THIS BOOK BELONGS TO:

____

The Hill We Climb

When day comes we ask ourselves,
where can we find light in this never-ending shade?
The loss we carry,
a sea we must wade.
We've braved the belly of the beast,
We've learned that quiet isn't always peace,
and the norms and notions
of what just is
isn't always just-ice.
And yet the dawn is ours
before we knew it.
Somehow we do it.
Somehow we've weathered and witnessed
a nation that isn't broken,
but simply unfinished.
We the successors of a country and a time
where a skinny Black girl
descended from slaves and raised by a single
mother
can dream of becoming president
only to find herself reciting for one.
And yes we are far from polished.
Far from pristine.
But that doesn't mean we are
striving to form a union that is perfect.
We are striving to forge a union with purpose,
to compose a country committed to all cultures,
colors, characters and
conditions of man.
And so we lift our gazes not to what stands

between us,
but what stands before us.
We close the divide because we know, to put our future first,
we must first put our differences aside.
We lay down our arms
so we can reach out our arms
to one another.
We seek harm to none and harmony for all.
Let the globe, if nothing else, say this is true,
that even as we grieved, we grew,
that even as we hurt, we hoped,
that even as we tired, we tried,
that we'll forever be tied together, victorious.
Not because we will never again know defeat,
but because we will never again sow division.
Scripture tells us to envision
that everyone shall sit under their own vine and fig tree
and no one shall make them afraid.
If we're to live up to our own time,
then victory won't lie in the blade.
But in all the bridges we've made,
that is the promise to glade,
the hill we climb.
If only we dare.
It's because being American is more than a pride we inherit,
it's the past we step into
and how we repair it.

We've seen a force that would shatter our nation
rather than share it.
Would destroy our country if it meant delaying
democracy.
And this effort very nearly succeeded.
But while democracy can be periodically delayed,
it can never be permanently defeated.
In this truth,
in this faith we trust.
For while we have our eyes on the future,
history has its eyes on us.
This is the era of just redemption
we feared at its inception.
We did not feel prepared to be the heirs
of such a terrifying hour
but within it we found the power
to author a new chapter.
To offer hope and laughter to ourselves.
So while once we asked,
how could we possibly prevail over catastrophe?
Now we assert,
How could catastrophe possibly prevail over us?
We will not march back to what was,
but move to what shall be.
A country that is bruised but whole,
benevolent but bold,
fierce and free.
We will not be turned around
or interrupted by intimidation,
because we know our inaction and inertia

will be the inheritance of the next generation.
Our blunders become their burdens.
But one thing is certain,
If we merge mercy with might,
and might with right,
then love becomes our legacy,
and change our children's birthright.
So let us leave behind a country
better than the one we were left with.
Every breath from my bronze-pounded chest,
we will raise this wounded world into a wondrous one.
We will rise from the gold-limbed hills of the west.
We will rise from the windswept northeast,
where our forefathers first realized revolution.
We will rise from the lake-rimmed cities of the midwestern states.
We will rise from the sunbaked south.
We will rebuild, reconcile and recover.
And every known nook of our nation and
every corner called our country,
our people diverse and beautiful will emerge,
battered and beautiful.
When day comes we step out of the shade,
aflame and unafraid,
the new dawn blooms as we free it.
For there is always light,
if only we're brave enough to see it.
If only we're brave enough to be it.

AMANDA GORMAN

Made in United States
North Haven, CT
19 December 2021